'Moon Faced Witch'
Edition 2

Published April 2019
Registered with Copyright House
Paperback e-book and audio
Illustrations from Shutterstock
On licence from various artists
Illustrations by Jenny Jop and Karen Stone

Audio edited and sound effects
By Micky Waters at HP media

ISBN Paperback 978-1-5272-3990-6
ISBN Audio 978-1-5272-3807-7
ISBN e-book 978-1-3867-8381-7

Moon Faced Witch
By Karen Stone

Chapter 1
The palace at Evergreen hill

The witch had a face
White and pale as the moon
These days, twigs and sticks
Were her knife fork and spoon
Her hair curled into ringlets
And had once shone like a flame
Her sister had hair exactly the same

Her father had been a kind mighty King
The white witch had memories
Of hearing birds sing
In a palace of colours that sparkled and gleamed

A life full of joys and smiles
So it seemed
Back then
The knives forks and spoons had been gold
But the story went sour
And that's what'll be told

The witch, hair like the sun
Had been born with a gift
To brighten the future
And help heal a rift

To bring neighbours together
If they'd had a fight
She used her skills
To make a wrong into a right

No-one knew
Why her teeth were so blue
Or her eyeballs
The colour of spinach you'd chew

I can't tell you the witch
Was pretty or sweet
But to mend broken friendships
Was an envious feat

One day when the sun
Orbed bright in the sky
A man strode into the palace with his pet
A small fly
The fly winked and smiled at the witch
And gestured to her
To meet in the ditch

The ditch surrounded the palace and so
The witch followed the fly
To squat and to know
What the strange buzzy being wanted to say
As she was curious, wide eyed
As fly's legs did splay

It settled itself and started to whisper
'I have much to divulge my ancient wise sister'!
'Sister'!
The witch squealed with delight, some surprise

For she'd had nothing to do
With insects or flies
'Have you wondered strange child
Why you have such a gift?

To heal the future
And through quarrels can sift'?
'Why no', squeaked the witch
Her voice jiggery and shrill

As she gazed with pea eyes
Onto evergreen hill
At this point in the story
The man with the fly

Loomed over the witch
And filled up the sky
Like a dark, jagged mountain
He blocked out the sun
His teeth yellow and sharp

Of pure intentions
There were none
He pulled a grey sack, over her head
Started to drag her, till her left knee bled

Chapter 2
The Kidnapping

Once out of the ditch
He whistled his donkey
Put the sack in a box
Locked it with a long key

The witch howled in the box
Dark and dank
She was scared
The donkey foul mouthed
Ears twitched, nostrils flared

The man strapped the box
On top of the beast
Leapt onto its back, which smelt of yeast
The small fly did hover, over the man

Till they reached evergreen hill
Then the land it did span
A huge chunk of the Earth
Shrivelled and sagging
The thirst of the soil
Blatant and nagging

The man, his eyes chips of Quartz
Whipped stinky donkey
Along the dry course
Where the ground moaned and cracked

Under its hooves
Donkey's joints ached as it crankily moved
The man followed red fly
As insect was master
Till the day turned to night, faster and faster

At last they all halted, exhausted and chilled
Small fly clung to a tree
The wind dropped, branches stilled
The witch's tears streaked her face

Mouth downturned in
Confined space
The box was set down,
Onto the caked dirt
The stillness was soothing
But her legs did so hurt

The witch drifted to snoring
Her dreams vivid and gnawing
The fly's silken eyelids slid over emerald eyes
Its task almost done, it gave a few sighs

The man, open mouthed, died
There in his sleep
His donkey rolled on him
Worn out, stank, so meek

The crimson of the sunrise
Stroked the edge of Earth
The witch blinked scratchy eyes open
And wept anew, for her hearth

Sorely missing her parents
And the palace so coloured
She banged on the box lid
And this is what followed

The small fly took off and sat on the man
Where it flicked out the long-key
From his pocket of sand
The donkey rocked rickety onto his hooves

Nipped the key with its teeth
Shoved the key to its groove
The box lid sprang open
Donkey gnashed at the sack
As he tugged it fell open

Out the witch spat
Open mouthed, lips widely quivering
As she wailed she started shivering
Finally, opening one spinach coloured eye
She was horrified to see

That right in front of her, the fly
Was growing large and bulbous
Changing with a huge fuss
Into a girl with curls
She finished with a whirl

The transformation was complete
Her milky mirror image
Took a seat, the orange ringlets bounced
The same pea eyes lit

Then smirked and danced
'I'll explain it all to you'
Said the girl who'd changed from fly
'We're sisters through and through'

The witch's eyes did widen
As her sister came a-sliding
Across the ground towards her on her knees
'You see my sibling dear
You crawled away, mum thought you near'

'No, it cannot be',
The witch haughtily exclaimed
'I have my parents and was duly named'
'Your name, sweet one is Chandra yin

I know I've put you in a spin
My name is Surya yang
We've been twins since time began
We revere Earth Water Fire and Wood!
This is all, for The Good
We value Metal
Precious gems left in the ground
I know you'll surely come around
To the idea as it is meant

The Earth's lush bounty is only lent
For we're all here for just awhile
Guardians, to put on file
All the wrongs done to the ground
I think I know just how this sounds

I need to take you back to home
Through rugged land and layers of loam
For you have a task to complete
So we need our feet to be fast and fleet

Alas!
We lost you young
But believe my honest tongue
The past is gone and done

I tell the truth and need to teach
Certain lessons
For you to reach
A higher purpose in your life
Which up to now's, had little strife

Our Mother is a great white Witch who
Shaman like can turn and switch
Into a fly or wolf or eagle
A cockerel or snouty beagle'

'Goodness me', the witch wide eyed
No longer for the palace cried
But got up and did start to follow her twin sister
Down the hollow, up the dale
Through the meadow
Sun then hail, gold then shadow

Meanwhile, the sad king moaned and strode
Around his multi- hued abode
Fretting
As to where his blue toothed daughter was

His wife, with raven sheet of hair
Eyes the colour
Of storm and hare
Paced and frowned and wept aloud
'Send the servants through the crowd!'

She begged the Monarch
The king's men rode hard in nearby country
But all they saw was a man with box
On his paunchy donkey

'Our daughter has been stolen'
The King had spoken
'Gone!
My heart is cracked, my sun not shone'
The King lamented, mind deeply dented

'Oh woe', she of the Raven hair
Now fidgeted and twisted
No longer lovely but coiled and wistful
Grieving for the child she'd known
Little knowledge she'd been born of crone

Chapter 3
The journey

Far away in a dappled glade
The witch thought of the King and his wifely maid
The witch had been blessed
To have been their child
For years before she'd crawled into the wild

There a giant bear so black
Swallowed her whole
In a belly of slack
This beast ambled for many weeks

Past fields of leeks
Avoiding the spiders who had terrible
Ideas
About trapping the bear and eating him there

A hunter pulled his bow one day
For his King the man did slay, that bear
On tugging off the bears full fur
Preparing the meat
To be cured
The queen's plump cook hauled out a baby
Who grew into a pea eyed young lady

The ringletted child was hugged
Loved and styled
The queen had known
That her womb was barren

This had for years
Pierced like a talon
The green eyed, flame haired curious child
Uplifted the couple, who daily smiled

They were impressed
With her mediating skills
As she diligently worked
Without airs or frills

Solving serious disputes and family feuds
Meant brocades from folk
Gifts of tasty foods
Jewels adorned their hair and shoes

The sparkling rubies
Diamonds so bright
Did not impress the witch
Although they were a sight

Witch preferred to wander
Through evergreen hill
Talking to mice and yellow parrots so shrill
With the wind whispering low
With her toes in the brook
She felt content as spruces shifted and shook

And so now here she was
Enthralled by her twin
Who nimble and joyous
Slipping like tuna with fin
Through stream and dense forest
They journeyed in

Wild blueberries popped, under the tongue
They narrowly avoided being mightily stung
By the bumbling bees
Who careened this way and that
Vibrantly buzzing, sunny stripy and fat

Walnuts so grooved, did surely prove
That the wilderness, provided food
When it became dark
Tawny owl they did hark

And crawled under the roots of an oak
The tree when it spoke
Soothed the small folk
So they drifted to dreams of sure hope

When the morning light dappled the roots
They laughed aloud at wild pigeon hoots
Then scrambled out
Yanked on felted boots
Sun crept through the canopy of leaves above
A squirrel twitched near then along glided a dove

'You have my gift witch, of creating peace
Your shaman mother waits along with my niece
Together your task will unfold and be finished'
Then off Uma flew to search for more spinach

'Daunting, this sounds'
Squeaked the witch who'd been found
Inside the bears belly
Now her legs turning to jelly

'Fear not', grinned her twin
'With our skills we will win
Now we must make haste
As no time to waste'

As they wished beige owl well
And drank from the river
They felt they'd been followed
It gave them a shiver
Right up their pale spines disturbing their minds
As the leaves rustled on their left
Something shuffled, sounding bereft

Donkey fell out. 'I come in peace'!
He offered them
A widening smile, sporting yellow teeth
Tomb like in style

'I have no place to settle
And need somewhere to apply my mettle
Can I travel as companion?
Although I am no stallion'

Chapter 4
Smelly donkey

The sisters knew the yeasty stink
Of the donkey who did think
That he could journey on with them and
Leave behind the world of Men

'Of course my fleabag friend
But first we'll surely tend
To giving you a scrub
And a serious rub a dub'

They led the grimy grey beast
To a place he had seen least
Into the centre of the river
Here they used a porcupine
Who really didn't mind

To comb the donkey's coat
Decades of filth and dust
Had turned into foul crust
So the witches used their elbows
To remove it

They rolled donkey through the river
Him, snorting with a shiver
Until he stood all spiky and sublime
Finally
With mint tugged from the river's edge
They polished teeth till glistening ledge

They then gathered marjoram
Tufts of wool from lamb
To anoint the donkey's skin
He, grateful and so sleek
Tossed his head no longer meek
And ready for adventure

'We must hurry scented friend
For just around that bend
Is a grove that could be awkward
If we do not race on forward'

Donkey trotted like a Sprite
Unaware of doomed and pending fight
For as the three scarpered round the bend
In front and side what did portend

Were giant spiders
Red and hairy
Joyless eyes with gaze so scary
Bristly hairs and crooked joints
At the end of eight legs
Sharp black points

Chapter 5
Tragedy at spider's lair!

The arachnids, woken early
Grimaced, bitter churlish
Saw before them a nubile meal
And three souls that they could steal

'I must change into fly'
Screamed the twin who told no lies
'A terrible idea'!
Squeaked her sister trembling near

As red fly ascended high, a huge spider
Plucked her from the sky and began
With precise skill, to prepare her meal
First she spun a silky thread
Then knit a web of ominous dread

The small fly writhed to no avail
The donkey shrieked and chased his tail
Around and round he circled till sick
Donkeys, when scared, do simply
Panic!

Aghast, the twin who still stood free
Wailed, blue teeth high up at the trees
From whence swooped down the sagely owl
Who detested the spiders, predatory and foul

With talons hooked into her gown
Owl lifted Chandra up off the ground
And flew up
High above foliage
Among chattering monkeys and biting midge

The owl let go of the dribbling witch
And a tufty brown monkey
Grabbed her without hitch
Proceeded to pass her to his uncle chimp
Who threw witch up onwards
Now unconscious and limp

Thirty chimps passed Chandra over the trees
While the shrill pitch of parrots
Spread the news
She'd been freed

By dusk a monkey
Set the witch down
She was grateful
So thankful, but groaned with a frown

'What of my twin and the donkey so fragrant'?
'I have no idea, the spider's a vagrant'
With that disturbing line, the monkey so fine
Lithe limbs so lean leapt up, as was keen
To get home

Meanwhile, donkey's nightmare
Had reduced him to a mess
Owl now glanced down, had to confess
That he felt both souls were surely doomed
Donkey's woeful face so full of gloom

Surya Yang was webbed in hate
Falling deeper into the throes
Of a fetid, mist filled state
Owl then observed as he flew

Glided and swerved
That the donkey sat untouched
And was therefore, as such
Able to escape

In donkey's fright he'd vomited and was a sight
As the contents of his stomach
Festered all around him
In small columns
He'd lost his fight

The spiders were repulsed by vomit
Donkey sagged both in and on it
They ventured not
Into the oval of sick and snot
Even they could not stand so close
To stinky donkey, scared and morose

Donkey's eyeballs wide, watched with fear
As the bristly spiders jostled near
Then they settled into slumber
Donkey's stomach stopped its rumble

He took a chance, lurched to his hooves
Kneecaps unbalanced with jerky moves
He zigzagged through the undergrowth
Until he bumped into a pink eyed sloth

'Tell me sloth, be quick, concise'
Then from behind the sloth crept two white mice
'Where is the village close to here?
I must gallop and speedily steer

To ask for help to free my friend
From flesh eating spiders around the bend'
The sloth, with sympathy did slowly speak
'Donkey, of vomit, old carrots you reek

To reach the village is difficult
If you take a wrong turn you'll be at fault
For a fee the mice will act as guide
As inside your ears they both will ride

Shouting out the surest route so like an arrow
You will shoot
Through the woods and to the village
Beware the boulders on yellowing ridge'

'Thank you Sloth'! The donkey bowed
His smelly snout so caked and fouled
The mice ran up his sticky haunches
Scuttled up his back

Along his paunches
To reside one in each waxy ear
Where they proceeded
To giggle and sneer

Chapter 6
Chandra yin the king's witch in the village

The King's witch meanwhile
Tumbled through hedges
Crawled through a cave
Along boulder full ledges

She found herself
On a mountainside
Fell on her butt
Started to slide

Through pebbles
Mud and slippery scree
In her haste to be free
Grazed her other knee

Sobbing for her enmeshed twin
She hurtled on her bruised
Raw skin
Until the convoluted path so ended
She stopped

And rubbed her legs and tended
To the cuts across her limbs
Rubbed her fingers along encrusted rims
Of bloodshot eyes
Breath now loud as sighs

Warily, she journeyed on
Entered a village, greeted by a swan
'Child you look in need of a bath
Your eyeballs are scarlet

You've suffered much wrath
Follow me and we will talk
Your legs are a state
Like motley stalks'

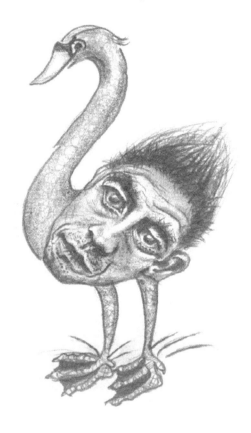

The man who owned the swan
Cast his narrow eyes upon the One
Who'd break his heart, leave him in sorrow
But that's a tale, for the morrow

He fell smitten
With lurching heart
From his senses he did part
Falling in love with yellow bruised witch

'Marry me, fiery haired wench
We will sit together on my yew bench
With many children at our feet
I will be replete, complete'

'Alas I can't, though you are handsome
I come to you to beg for ransom
To free my witchy, troubled twin
Wrapped in poisonous web
Declining, thin

For if I leave her there to rot
I'll forever be sad and with no joy, no not
Able to smile or enjoy my life
So sturdy man, I can't be your wife'

With that the male flew to a temper,
Gripped the witch
No thought to tempt her
But to keep her close to him

His heart was full, to the brim
Of longing
That of which now not returned
His heart smouldered
Then flared and burned

Into a room he trapped the witch
This was not love for it had switched
To something false
Of ownership

And for the witch it did nip
Any hope of freedom in the bud
She fell to the bed
With a thud

For many days the witch just slept
Frightening dreams, spiders in nest
Of a milky skinned, near absent mother
She awoke feeling in, a spot of bother

Finally, the man entered the room
Started with a bristly broom
To stretch the witch's jaw so wide
He still thought she'd be his bride

But first he felt he'd scrub her teeth
This made Chandra yin, struggle and seethe
'These teeth are unnatural
They must be washed white'
'No'! Shrieked the witch, ready to fight

Wrestling the broom
From the burly mans hands
Jumped on it then
Flew over the lands
She'd had no idea she could do such a thing

With her thoughts and intentions
She was able to cling
Onto the broom
First it had traversed past the door
Then banged the walls
Maniacally skidded, across the floor

Then she was free, flying through clouds
Blue teeth like sky, gazing on down
Onto mounds of fecund lush land
The wind the only rushing sound

Land full of sheep
That looked small as leeches
She squinted over, large sandy beaches
And onto vast teal blue coloured oceans
When the brooms lurching motions

Made the witch queasy
The journey less easy
So with her mind, she was able to find
That she could fly lower and lower
Till broom wobbled, got slower
And careened towards Earth

In her rollicking fear she let go of the broom
Plummeting down, sensing impending doom
Then landing ungainly, struggling vainly
Into the twigs of a beech tree

Her flame coloured locks
Were snarled into blocks
That knotted and tangled and kept her
From freeing herself
From that woody shelf

Feeling so weary, beyond even teary
She succumbed to sleep
Dreamless and deep, cradled in bark
Sky darkening, night stark

Chapter 7
Twin Surya yang and the hares

Back at spider's lair
Postured a huge hare
He led a band of spritely young ones
With sinewy legs and full, bright strong lungs

Into the spider's camp
Where they built a ramp
Up to the spider's nest
Where the witch's sorry rest
Had turned her ashen white
A most disturbing sight

The hares had long strong white teeth
That their ancestors had so bequeathed
While the spider squat, slept deep, eyes closed
Those hares, they climbed and up they rose

They tore at the web that held the witch
Who free at last began to itch and
Scratch her milky pale white skin
Eyeballs bulging and so thin

From the spider's frightful frown
Taking her to a glimmering cave
She cried and grateful for the save

That meant she'd live and breathe, be free
To do all the things she hoped with glee
They fed her hazelnuts from the woods
And day by day improved her moods

Till she was well enough to travel
And find her twin and so unravel
The tale that had gone so very wrong
Making their journey far too long

The witch found she could no longer turn
Into a fly so began to yearn
That one day she could try again
To buzz and zoom around and spin

The hares asked her to kneel
Wound cowslip round her heels
Used an ash twig to strengthen
After Surya's ordeal

The cowslip, beloved plant
Would help give renewed strength
As the battle that was looming
Might go on for dreadful length
Around her head as a flowering crown
Hares placed a headdress of foxglove
Primrose, wild thyme

The hares blew out wax candles
From deep in the cave
Blessed the white witch
From near death

A close shave
Sent her on her way sat on a tortoise
With magic twig of ash
There'd be no headlong rush

To say farewell the hares tickled her neck
The tortoise then began to check
He was on the right path
To return witch to her hearth

Lumbering slowly along forest floor
The witch felt an anger flare at her core
The spiders had robbed her of days of her life
She vowed to return to slay them with knife

To stop them from stealing
Any more souls
They would be vanquished
And burnt with hot coals

Chapter 8
Donkey reaches the village

The donkey guided by the mice
Cut through the forest as he did slice
Through brambles, leaves and across streams
In his head imagined witch's screams
Thinking her a pulpy meal
Distraught was how he now did feel

Cantering into the village saw swan
The mice took a dive, into the sun
Glad to be out of moist tickly ears
They went searching for old friends
They'd known for years

'Why donkey, what is it you seek'?
Curtsied the swan, snow feathered and sleek
'I'm looking for a moon faced witch'
He spoke with frown and nervous twitch

'The one you speak of with flaming hair
Did pass through here and was snared
By a man of town who kept her hidden
I spied all this as I hid in the midden'

'Oh dear', the donkey grimaced
As rain now drizzled in a fine mist
'How will I ever rescue her'?
'No need', said rat, 'She left in a blur'

'Agape!
I saw her flying off and will never again
Sneer or scoff
At tales of witches on a broom
For this one took off
From inside the room'!

'I must be off then to continue
For my witches care I must not dwindle'
'Farewell'
The swan's neck bowed and arced
As her friend, a swift fine lark

Alighted and told of what he'd seen
Witches fall from broom and wild careen
Into a wood of mighty beeches
'I'll take you but beware the leeches'

The lark did speak to donkey clear
'They'll suck your blood till you are near
A drained weak end, you'll turn to bone
After a week of pain and moan'

The lark found upon the donkey's back
A comfy perch, he had the knack
Of helping others with their woes
Healing them when they suffered blows

The bird sang in voice so sweet and pure
The donkey just had to confer
He'd never heard a sound so bright
As he trotted off into the night

Chapter 9
Chandra yin in the forest of beeches

As the king's witch awoke
She heard a croak
Saw before her on a branch
A purple toad as if by chance
He looked askance

Was then gobbled in one mouthful
By a snake whose job it was to
Cull purple toads and scarlet frogs
It was a most agreeable job

The snake was blue and dry, so quiet
Slithering silently as thought it might
Decide to swallow the witch as well, but no
He reckoned his insides would swell

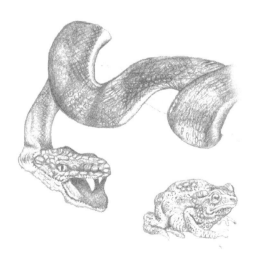

To proportions from which
He may never recover
So instead he concluded
He'd have to shove her
As she couldn't remain
In his solitary domain

'You appear, green eyed girl
To be trapped in my house
Up here in my beech
I doze and eat grouse'

'I fell from my broom'
The witch spluttered with lustre
All of her dignity
She attempted to muster

'No doubt'
Smirked small serpent
And using forked tongue
He chopped chewed dismantled

The witch from her bung
Of strands of her hair
Caught up in the beech
The witch now was free

And did start to beseech
'Don't eat me blue snake
As I have to make
A journey to mother

We've had awful bother and
I must find sister
I have sorely missed her
Also find donkey

Who really quite frankly
Could be a hindrance
Who was useless that once
When surrounded by spiders in lair'

'I really don't care', yawned the snake
But beware, if you stay for much longer
I may stoke a hunger so climb down this tree
Then my history you'll be'

The snake had recognised the little witch
He thought her the daughter
Of the One
That could switch

To any beast of the land
That she so chose
If he hurt twin he dreaded
To think what he'd lose

Hastily witch clamoured down
Until her feet were on the ground
Avoiding leeches,
Dodging beeches

She ran awhile then paused to sip
From a stream
Then started to skip
Along a path she knew of old

There in front of her, behold, her mother
Who she prayed would not scold
As she'd returned without her sibling
But felt so happy
That she just wanted to sing

'Oh daughter, I can't believe my eyes
I flew as Eagle through ebony skies
I could not find you or see you in mind
Were you in a terrible bind?
What news of your sister? Tell me

I'll tend blister, around your big toe
Now mind, tell it slow'
Chandra yin did recount
With gravity and pout
All that had passed
Now she was home at last

The mother spoke with tenderness
'Child your hair's an unruly mess
But you do look just like your sister'
Up leapt young witch and duly kissed her

'Enough of my past, will my sister last?
I fear that right now
The spiders will not allow
Her to leave their filthy den
What will happen then'?

'Ah, so that's where she is!
I must hurry and whizz
I've no time to instruct you as to Eagle
I have to

Soar and release her
Then concoct the right cure
To counter spiders venom
Then return home with aplomb'

'Tell me mother before you fly
With outstretched wings
Through inky sky
Why did you and sister kidnap me?

After you could rightly see
That I was well and in good health
Why on earth go to the trouble
Of all that stealth'?

'The migrating birds told us of your survival
They relayed your story as they'd had an eyeful
We reckoned you just wouldn't journey home
To a life of simple spell spinning crone

We thought the king's men
Would come searching for you
So we hid you in the box
So they never knew

We kept it from you
So it looked like a kidnap
Then when you'd journeyed far
We released you from that trap

We hired that man
His donkey in tow
Your sister turned fly
And so now you know

Perhaps it wasn't wise
But once you know the size
Of the task that you've been called for
You'll realise that it's a special large chore

Chapter 10
Eagle in flight

The shaman witch did start to twitch
In front of her child
Grew feathery and wild
Till with beak sharp as dagger

She stretched and with swagger
Extended full wings
And with the freedom that brings
Took to the treetops

As the lark sang sweetly on donkey's fur
He glimpsed the Eagle, swift shifting spur
'I recognise that noble bird'
The donkey turned as he had heard
The urgency in lark's voice

Donkey stopped and made no noise
'Wait here' instructed lark
As he shimmied up into the bark
Of a graceful willow tree

Where he met his friend the flea
'Jump in my feathers, you may be of aid
We must catch up with Eagle
So we'll fly like a blade'

Chapter 11
Flying high

The flea leapt in a second under lark's feather
Hoping there wouldn't be inclement weather
He detested rain snow hail and sleet
It made him so grumpy and cold with damp feet

Up the pair soared
Chasing dynamic eagle
Flea started to daydream
About cake and treacle

As the wind whistled by
He grew rather peckish
Pray we reach eagle
Was flea's fervent strong wish

Then I can hop down
From lark's silken feather
Find my friend Brighid gnat
Then, together

We can search for moist sponge with custard
That's when flea spotted the mean
Spiteful buzzard
The buzzard had an ego the size of a planet

None of the other birds
Could really understand it
It's true he was ugly and actually seemed shy
But no one could tell

The reason why
He shoved and he pushed other birds away
So lived alone
In a barrel of dung and hay

The flea felt concern
As the buzzard mid flight turned
With a beady glint in its eyes
It careened, through the skies
Straight at the lark

Who could see plain and stark
That the buzzard was angry and up for a fight
With all its might the buzzard in flight
Aimed at the lark who like a spark

Shot out of its way and sped on, no delay
'That bird is an annoying bully
The turquoise sky he'll always sully'
Thought Udgitha the lark

The flea had lost his appetite
Breathed a sigh of relief that there'd be no fight
He doubted if buzzard would get second chance
To send quick lark off course uneven, askance

Chapter 12
Surya yang and her tortoise

The twin witch who'd escaped the spider's trap
Awoke bleary eyed from a nap
The tortoise's rocking motion had mesmerised
But she was still plotting the spider's demise

'I will return one day to murder the spiders'!
She spluttered with fury erupting from inside her
'The poison of anger and betrayal, deep hurt
Will rise up one day and from you could spurt

Or it may fester inside you
And coil then reside there
Until it turns you to skull
Your body a shell'

Said the tortoise
'You must forgive the red arachnids
They are being themselves
And only the Elves, can lead them away

To rekindle your hate
Means bad thoughts will abate
And make you quite ill
If you plan to kill
Those large spiders for thrill'

The moon faced witch
Said she would consider
The tortoise's wise words
As well he did bid her

The lark and flea
Momentarily
Lost sight of the witch
To eagle had switched

The witch as eagle had decided
To pay a visit to one, much derided
Witch knew blue snake from way before
A hundred years ago or more

As she alighted now upon the beech
She intended to deliver a weighty speech
'Oh you', hissed snake
Rolling his eyes
'The witch with many a cunning disguise'

'I've come to thank you
For freeing my daughter
She has a job to do
To prevent bloodshed and slaughter

The twins were born
To perform a dangerous task
Now I must tell you
That I've come to ask
For assistance

As your time has finally come
To rise up from the dust
You're the one I will trust
So help us you must

You snakes and Naga have always been
Guardians of gifts so pure, unseen
Protectors of sacred and precious things
My news of battle to you I bring

A Great War is coming
And deep inside you
Is a mighty adversary
Cunning and cursory

I'll call on you snake Bheda
When the time comes
Peel those toads and frogs
From your slimy gums'

Small serpent thought awhile then said
'Aye great witch, war makes us dread
I'll be there for you to do your bidding
But in exchange for one daughter
And a wedding'

'I'll turn you to warrior with my inspired spells
You'll marry my child as your fine chest swells
Consider it done snake! I'll call for you soon
I'll send my white dove on the night of full moon

Uma Dove will deliver a message
That the plans have begun
Then you'll come and victor
Like you were my son'

Chapter 13
Donkey's transformation

Donkey became quite agitated as he shifted
Whinnied and then waited
Convinced the lark had abandoned him
He unsteadily cantered to the rim

Of a giant crater
Where seconds later
He saw an eagle far from meagre
Like an arrow, true proud not callow

Donkey ran around the crater
Which took an hour and
Was a deflator
At last he entered into woods with beeches

Where he spied the suckling leeches
Petrified!
Started to gallop
Through the trees, at great speed

Breathless and now fairly tired
He stumbled into a prickly briar
As he attempted to backtrack from that
He glimpsed a wizard in an orange hat

The hat was long with a point on the end
The wizard was drunk, he couldn't pretend
'Well what brings you here, ugly mule?
Don't stare at me so it's rude and quite cruel'
'I beg your pardon Mr Wizard'

Donkey saw he had a lizard, as a footstool
Drunk as well, the reptiles eyes began to swell
Then bulge and wobble before they closed
Bored, he thought he'd have a doze

'I do believe I've one more spell
For your lame looks I will dispel
Hocus Pocus! newt and thorn
There! You're now a Unicorn'

With a flash that blinded donkey
He felt searing heat and very wonky
As he peered down upon his hooves
He blinked, as if to somehow prove

To himself, that he was still grey fur, but no
Now absolutely sure
He gazed at long white legs of horse
From his forehead, shaft of horn, of course

Donkey had just disappeared
His fuzzy grey coat
Had been cleared
Instead a gleaming coat of white
He'd have to go and find a knight

The wizard reached for his brown bottle
'Well that was clever', he said, as toppled
And tipped heavy through the briars' tangle
His arms and legs a disjointed mangle

The bottle flew from wrinkled hand
Where it sailed through the air
Then did plonkily land, onto inebriated lizard
Who'd been dreaming of a lilac blizzard

Where he had rescued a reptile so fierce
His heart had been struck and then fully pierced
With a strong love only reptiles know
He woke from dream of purple snow

Furious!
So livid that he'd been woken
From dream so vivid
On seeing the bottle
The wizard had lost

He decided that as wizard
Had his way it tossed
Downed the sloe berries
That had made them so merry
As two years ago they'd drank all the sherry

The wizard's orange hat now tilted
Sunlight slanted down and filtered
Through the tangle of undergrowth
To show him in a posture
Most uncouth

Unicorn thought with amazement even
Through his temporary derangement
That wizard looked like the king's witch
As he lay splayed he began to twitch

'Begone you unicorn of white!
You've upset my reptile with your spite
Now leave my briar so I can sleep
I need a month to slumber deep'

Unicorn, once stinky donkey, trotted
Magnificently
Out of the wood where over brook
He stood and marvelled at his new look

He tossed his silky snowy mane
Chided himself for being vain
But really couldn't help it
As the wizard was the culprit

Unicorn so very pleased
His mouth broke open
To a crease
Of a most magnanimous grin
Enjoying uplifted mood he was now in

Chapter 14
Surya Yang's despair

Surya Yang and her tortoise
Didn't make much noise
As he was a plodder and so they ate cheddar
Enjoyed listening to woodpeckers and
Sparrow hecklers

They saw ants so busy
As they hastened
To make long delicious tasty food chains
To take back to their nests

Where their infants with gangly jest
Climbed on each other
With hinds of spindly legs
Munching and chewing on the forest dregs

'I'm sure we are nearing
The orange wizard's clearing
He is my cousin
And I must admit to fearing

That he'll be very drunk
His mood it will have sunk
We should really visit
As I need rest from biting midges'

The tortoise said
'Oh yeah,' as he had rightly guessed
That the witch was still recovering
From the turmoil

Of that other thing
Involving horrid spiders
She was full of hope
As she wanted to reach home
To her mother shaman crone

Dmitri lifted up his lid
With ancient belly and leathery mid
'Come crawl under here, you will be safe
No need to fret or worry or chafe

'We will sleep here tonight
Journey on once it's daylight'
A goblin crept up after dusk
The forest smelt of damp and musk

He yanked the witch out as she slept
Two more goblins with stealth they crept
The witch woke with a fright
The goblins an evil, bulbous nosed sight

This made the witch scream in distress
Goblins around her did now hard press
They wrapped vines from the forest
Around witch, who in yet another mess
Felt much despair, would she ever get there?

The tortoise, loyal but ancient
Had died in the night
Never complacent
He'd lived a long and helpful life
But had left the witch in horrid strife

Crying for home, through woody gloom
The goblins put her on the back
Of their mad skunks in a pack
Who carried her deep into the wood
Where she felt she'd come to no good

Chapter 15
The Unicorn

The lark and flea alighted gracefully
Onto a crooked tree
Who rolled up crinkly eyelids
To see who'd settled in its midst

'Wise tree', said flea
'Tell us what you saw in the silent dark
We seek an eagle and her witch daughter
We fear some beastly being has caught her'

This Elder tree had once been a witch
But for rest and respite
Had found a new niche
Tree rumbled

'I've heard a rumour through dappled leaves
When the forest was silent
Inward it cleaved
This is news I feel you both should believe

The goblins who feast on rotting meat
Stole a witch from a tortoise
A difficult feat
They bound her
Then laid her on the back of their skunks

Can the wizard help?
For ninety years he's been drunk!
It's said he failed to use his skills
To save the land near evergreen hill

The palace still stands with a wealthy court
Where they live unaware
But mainly feast and cavort
The king's father passed bounteous land

To men who were bound
To an unholy contract
To ruin land that now contracts
As it's thirsty and useless
So wizard sank to a sad mess'
Lark thanked and blessed the knowing tree
Took off from bark with musing flea

The unicorn had trotted proud
Across the wild and untamed land
He paused behind a verdant copse
As he watched a woodpecker

As he tapped and chopped
Into a tree who miserable said
'You've caused sharp pain inside my head!'

Unicorn stepped out to speak
'Woodpecker! Have you news for me
Of a witch with orange hair
Running through trees, white face so fair?

'I've seen one, aye, in sobbing state,
The goblins took her, who've eyes like slate
Travel swift, white horse with horn
Or you'll find your witch was a meal and torn

'That way'!
The woodpecker tossed hammering beak
As it continued to knock and to wreak
Havoc, on the tree's gnarled bark
Who eventually shook it off in a nark

The sleek white unicorn gathered speed
Galloped, handsome trusty steed
His nostrils open
All aquiver

As he burst into the goblin's den
They froze then began to fearfully shiver
Unicorn chased them, scattering creatures
With twisted hateful, devilish features

Until they'd yelped and skittered
Gone!
Horse chewed vines
Till witch's binds were undone

'Oh your eyes look familiar' said witch
She'd never felt sillier
But gained her composure
Now that her turmoil was over

'I feel awful about skunks
And goblins escapades'!
'Worry not, twin Surya
These bad memories will fade'

'I feel I know you'
Said the witch who'd given
The donkey a scrubbing
In the fast flowing river

'Yes child!
You'll never believe but a donkey I was
Grey furred and peeved
A wizard with weird orange hat
A lizard so drunk, under his feet sat

After wizard casting a spell
I'm unicorn now, fast strong and well
We must travel now!
I'm so glad to see you

We've had furrowed brow
Wondering where you were
You've suffered from spiders,
Skunks, goblin's curse'

'It could have been worse', sighed witch
'I know of the drunk as he is my cousin
We do need to see him
As he's full to the brim

Of self-loathing
Sadness, much shame
For the past
He's not to blame

So you were the donkey
Belonged to man with the long key
Who we hired to bring twin
Back home to kin'

Unicorn nodded
Hooves pawing the clod earth

'Oh unicorn with horn so long
I'm delighted you've come to take me home
Once my shaman mother sees you
She'll beg a favour for task to do

A battle is brewing, foul forces are spewing
Which we'll have to contain
If we are to remain
On our bounteous Earth'

Chapter 16
Home at last

For days the white horse
Surya yang on his back
Galloped, then rested
Stayed off the main track

Until, along path that she recognised
She jumped off the steed
To her surprise, her twin
Chandra yin, ran to embrace her
They'd both survived, of that they were sure

Chapter 17
Elves gathering with wolves

In a moist clearing
Of chamomile and comfrey
The elves met with the wolves
Who'd always been free
To rest with the elves

As part of their family
Now they had business to discuss
With bees, midges and fleas
Regarding the sacrifice of ancient wise trees

'The doves have informed us
Of the gathering men
Who intend to damage the Earth
Chop trees and then

Make a large profit
And sit fat and smug
We must finish them off
Feed their flesh to the slugs'!

The wolves padded along
Past glow worms and giant ferns
To tell all the animals of man's plan to burn
Their only home
They'd have to rebel and risk limb and bone
To save herbs and loam

A rippling caterpillar
With yellow and white stripes
Fell on a wolf's snout
Who talked to all types

Wolf felt all the creatures
Should really know
That the forest was heading
For a near fatal blow

'Caterpillar'! The wolf gruffly growled
'Slide off my snout
Tell the giant bear that scowls
The one they call Gallbladder
That he must stand up and roar on hind legs

On the day we meet the human dregs
Inform Gallbladder
That he must now tell the robins
Then they must fly round

Tell relatives and cousins
Who will pass this on to ravens and thrush
Wiggle away now!
News must travel in a rush'

An hour later Hecate caterpillar
Leapt off a lush green leaf
To Gallbladder the bears amazed disbelief
Landed onto his left eyeball
Acrobatic caterpillar
Hardly ever had a fall

'Gallbladder!
Here is my news from Lobo the wolf
The forest creatures must now plan to engulf
The men advancing to destroy our homes

We'll let them know
They'll end up in tombs
If they dare to snap a twig
Or damage us creatures
However small or big'

The bear and stripy acrobat
Nodded and talked not realising that
The buzzard was tucked up in his nearby barrel
Hidden by cowslip, giant ferns and sorrel

Once it was quiet
Buzzard sure they had left
He came out and took off
Saw the meeting with elves
Flying over the tip of the forest so lush
He landed in a clearing, shattering the hush

'Orange wizard come out!
It's your old friend grey buzzard'
Red eyed and wobbly, out crawled the lizard
The wizard followed on hands and knees
To see the buzzard, neither mightily pleased

'Give up your drinking
You've both become stinking
Your company so lame
The booze is to blame

We three need to be ready
For the big day
When we join in the battle
We must be sober not fey

The wizard took out his pestle
While the lizard gathered the nettles
Along with milkthistle and dandelion
To cleanse their livers, boost their iron

Due to the chatter of trees, birds
Wolves and monkey
The tale spread through the forest
Of witches and donkey
The story travelled of goblins, unicorn
Through the chatter of those, in forest born

They prepared to gather their wits and strengths
To prevent home from being flattened and fenced
The shaman witch eagle now weary and feeble
Turned on the wing buoyed by blackbirds that sing
In a melodious tune, eagle would be home soon

As she alighted near orange wizard clearing
Eagle thought she would rest, alas also fearing
That wizard her relative, she'd have to give
A magical funeral burning inside wild boar rib

Finding him healing and loudly snoring
The lizard was pointedly
Ignoring
The eagle as she went to settle
In a large bunch of medicinal nettles

She slept until the sun's rays crept
With yellow pointed fingers
The new days' bright harbringers
To the lizard said
'At last you both are sobering
You'll have heard of the foreboding

Tell wizard to be ready
Don't forget this message
Or I'll turn you to lizard sausage'
With a peck on his scaly shank

The lizard hopped, no longer stank
Eagle took to sky through cumulus clouds
Spatters of rain, her shadow darkening
Thick woods and plain

At last her claws gripped ground
Grateful there she found
Her twin daughters with powerful horse
Ready to battle
For now, struggle paused

Chapter 18
The meeting

Not far from the witch's fire
The world of men met to conspire
To burn the forest to the ground
Some men were unwise
Would not hear the sound
Of creatures pain

Men thought they'd pierce the Earth
Not realizing the awful curse
They'd leave behind
For the rest of mankind

They gathered now with tools of iron
Machinery stronger than any lion
With jagged metal teeth of steel
They tragically intended to peel
The forest floor from the Earth
For pleasures and monetary mirth

Around the fire the witch shaman knelt
Steaming kale, turmeric and spelt
'The men have gathered on sacred space
Tomorrow we will come face to face
With them, to make our firm minds known

We'll tell them nothing good can be grown
When they have ruined it for wealth
There'll be no medicinal herbs left
For good health'

The witch's dove flew down
From a rowan tree's fine crown
'The animals that live in this forest
Will need to gather with all their courage
We will stand up to fight this crime
We will prevail, now is the time'

The dove had flown to bring blue snake
Akhilandeshvari took him, began to shake
As witch, cast a most auspicious spell
That she would never share or tell

Before the twins and unicorn's eyes
A splendid sight, a strange surprise
Witch doubled over, her hair turned green
She clutched around her stomach and spleen

The snake began to writhe and spit
Then before them it squirmed in awful fit
Was thrown then, onto the fire
Emerged muscle bound warrior who'd never tire

Shaman mother spoke
'I promised to betroth you
To my daughter Surya yang
Now you are a warrior
No longer snake with fang

I bind you as a couple
Till the end of time
Now together we will battle
To end the mens' mad crime'
Snake warrior boomed in ringing voice

'Aye, we all make this choice'!
'I willingly give you my daughter
You will adore her without falter
You'll teach your offspring when they're born
That forest from Earth should not be torn'

They slept that night around fire smouldering
Whilst animals roamed, caring and scolding
Their young ones, who'd know the benefit
Of the battle looming, they'd not bear brunt of it

Chapter 19
The battle

As the dawn kissed infinite sky from
The undergrowth and tree tops high
Creatures from the forest and wood
Ventured to open land, hovered or stood

In defiance of the act of carnage
Of moss and tracks that creatures of all sizes
Had travelled, lived for thousands of years
Under ancient trees, who now had fears

The men who'd prepared
At the edge of green lush
Were halted, alarmed into a quiet eerie hush
Then swarms of bees, fleas and midges
Gathered over them in weird ridges

The sound of this was most disturbing
This was a sign for the elves to now bring
The giant spiders that they could ride
They controlled their minds so could sit astride

The crawly beasts with pointy legs
They scuttled forth, bristly bringers of death
Each elf held a porcupine
Ready to hurl as a fighting sign
At men who intended to destroy plants and oak

If the men didn't flee they'd end up with a cloak
Of the sharp porcupine quills, that pierced the skin
When thrown with measured
Precise skill

The youngest bravest of the elves
Drew a blade so long, no thought of self
He'd placed his sisters with bow and arrows
High in the trees and hidden in hollows

The sloth had taken much longer to
Join the angry livid throng who
Were readying for bloody battles
His mice were screeching and shaking bone rattles

Leopards and deer stood with wild boar
Destruction of forest they could not ignore
So now stood as one band
To save home and their land

Orangutans sat astride panthers
Nothing would stand in their way or hamper
Their victory
Choice to be free

Ular, snake warrior strode
With an army of wolves
Who were destined to grind terrible grooves
Into the bones of destructive humans
They were poised to threaten
Howl along with the shamans

There were no tigers left
Poachers had finished them off
Their friends felt bereft
Men had carried tigers aloft

The wizard with the orange hat
Had found in himself as sober he'd sat
One last spell to turn his reptile
Into a dragon with helmut of metal

The spellbound dragon stood tall as a horse
Now fire breathing dragon of menacing force
The wizard used his legs to grip
As he sat astride to prevent his slip

They hurtled out from behind a tree of Rowan
As all the birds of the forest flew
Flapping and crowing
Around the mens' heads'
As they ducked and cowered

Muscly hares bounded out of the bowers
That leapt at the men
Landing blows on their knees
As witch eagle took off
Out of a giant tree

Squirrels rode hard on beavers
Shouting, 'Go now and leave us'!
All manner of beetle and weevil
Crawled against the men's plans as so evil

The otters slid out of pure water
'We need homes for spouses, sons daughters'!
They cried from their hearts
From river's edge they'd not part

Parakeets, anteaters and moths
Ventured out from ground and treetop lofts
Butterflies, tickled the hides
Of cheetars that bounded out with fierce pride

The elephants charged
Giant rats on their backs
They had to prevent large trees being hacked
Rats spread Brazil nuts all through their land
They'd fight to stop forest
Turn into sand

They forgot all their arguments, fights
Joined forces, gathered all creatures in might
To save medicinal plants and herbs
So that mankinds' diseases would be curbed

Gallbladder the bear reared up high
Roared his disgust to the clouds and the sky
Chandra yin, king's witch emerged
Green eyes sharp and not perturbed

Eyes like glassy penetrating shafts
Astounded, men watched her approaching
With army vast
In her hands she drew bow and arrow
Her face gaunt, fierce and sallow

'We demand you leave right now
Or we will snarl and howl
Pick your flesh from bone
Until you're weak and done and gone'

Surya Yang rode up behind her
The unicorn under her firm fine rear
'Begone! You men of reckless morals
You best leave now or face what follows'

The buzzard sat so regal
On reptile dragon's head
A headdress of glinty eyed
Mean feathery dread
He would never allow them
To cut down the woods
Even with some birds he'd used to quarrel
He intended to make bonds
Leave his dung barrel

The wizard and buzzard turned dragon reptile
Towards the men with hostile hot bile
The clawed eagle swooped, grasped a man
Who held a chainsaw in his hand

Shaman witch eagle took him high in clouds
The man dropped his saw and screamed aloud
As she released him from talons sharp
The man fell into oak, grazed by its bark

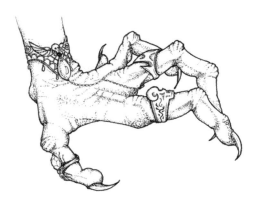

The oak turned inwards, wrapping branches
Twisted twigs around his body
Until he was trapped
Fearful and bloody

By now the men were scattering
As snake warrior waded in, breaking limbs
Chasing men, who had fully realised by then
As monkeys jumped upon their backs

They staggered shrieking down the tracks
That would lead them home to safety
If they still could run
They did so hastily

Chapter 20
Safe haven

In the years that followed
There was peace in the forest
Nature cradled all who lived there
They'd survived a hard test

Snake warrior and Surya yang lived long
Hearing Udgitha the lark's sparkling song
In their ears
Bearing seven children
To take up righteous spears

To protect sacred land from the ignorant few
Who felt the need to destroy, not renew
The root network of the earth
These seven grew in strength and mirth

The shaman mother with her relative the wizard
Had given all they had to give
They journeyed deep to the forest's centre
Where they jointly intended and
Really meant to

Sleep for at least a thousand years
Inside the trunk of an Elder
Who no longer feared
That it would be hacked and
Chopped to the floor

The witch knew the wizard would mightily snore
They both sorely needed to sleep
So left the forest
To natures sure keep

The unicorn took Chandra yin
Back through the woods to maid and king
Where they were overjoyed to greet them
Got on their knees to kiss the hem
Of the witch's brown hemp skirt

Appalled at this she had to blurt
'No, my king and raven haired beauty
I had to leave you to do my duty
Now I have returned to care for you both
Until you become grey and long in the tooth'

Whilst at the palace
A prince saw unicorn
Begged white horse to be his
Or he'd be forlorn

Sir Prancealot
Promised adventure and travel
They'd journey across oceans
New cultures would unravel

The white horse was hungry
For experiences new
He bade witch farewell and then in lieu
Of a kiss, he licked her face
It tasted of cheddar
Parsley and mace

Another decade of witch solving disputes
The seasons passed
Autumn leaves
Sun, spring shoots

The king and queen
Felt their waists become thicker
Then they passed away
Had requested burial in wicker

Where their bodies would be
Gifts absorbed back into the Earth
Witch no longer cared for the palace's hearth
So she left to abide with the parrots shrill and
The scampering mice on evergreen hill

Before she left the ancient plump cook
Put her red hands on witch as she cried and shook
'Stay well pea eyed women
I will miss you! I give you a black kitten
I've named her Chewchew'

The witch tucked Chewchew
Under her armpit
Where the fluff ball peeked out
To watch beetles sit

In slants of sun shafts
Outside palace walls
The witch walked away
From silk and banquet halls

On evergreen hill
She felt calm and safe
Bed of leaves, lichen and moss
No sense of sadness or loss

Ants played through her spiralling hair
The squirrels brought nuts
That they wanted to share
The leader of the wolves would daily visit
They'd lie across his back
Watch sparrows fly, flit

Through multi-hued greens
She'd enjoy just breathing
The witch forgot the past
When rapturous and kneeling

The witch had a face
White and pale as the moon
These days, twigs and sticks
Were her knife fork and spoon
Her hair curled into ringlets
And once shone like a flame
Her sister had hair exactly the same

The End

NOTES

Trees absorb the greenhouse gas carbon dioxide from our atmosphere. They are the lungs of our world. Greenhouse gases are contributing to climate change. Deforestation is one of the factors causing and worsening climate change. Half of the world's tropical forests have been cleared for timber, to grow the cash crops palm oil, soya and coffee and to graze cattle for the consumption of beef. Many species of animals and insects will soon be extinct. Orangutans are maimed and lose their homes. Many have died. I have purposefully made the ending violent to instil in the reader the panic and pain of everything that lives in a wood or forest as it burns or is destroyed by machinery. My ending is obviously the opposite of what's been happening for decades. The ice caps on the globe are melting at an alarming rate due to climate change. When trees are burned and cut down soil erosion takes place and there are more floods and landslides. Poor people suffer greatly from these catastrophes. Sign petitions online to prevent large corporations from continuing to destroy forests. Donate to Green peace, organisations and charities that fight this destruction.

Dictionary for Moon Faced Witch

Abandon. *Leave, stop looking after someone, desert them, give up*

Adversary. *An opponent in a conflict, contest or dispute*

Agape. Mouth wide open in surprise or wonder, unbalanced

Agitated. *Feeling or appearing troubled or nervous*

Apex. Top of or highest part of something

Aplomb. *Self confidence, assurance in a difficult situation*

Appalled. *Greatly dismayed or horrified*

Arachnids. *Spiders*

Ash tree. *Very strong tough, elastic wood Historical, mythical importance to Vikings and British It was thought to have protective, healing and magical qualities. It symbolises the World tree which was a tree that joined the three worlds: the underworld, the middle earth and the spiritual realm Ash tree was used to aid children with weak limbs in ancient times*

Askance. *Suspiciously, with a look of disapproval, doubtful, mistrust*

Bereft. *Feeling sad and lonely, deprived of or lacking something*

Bile. *Fluid that aids digestion and is secreted by the liver and stored in the gall bladder*

Bile. *Anger, bitterness, hatred*

Bower. *A shady place under trees, a wood or garden*

Briar. *Prickly, scrambling shrubs or plants*

Brocade. *Richly woven fabric with raised pattern with gold or silver thread*

Bung. *Stopper or plug, to have an accident*

Buoyed. *Lifted up, make someone cheerful or confident*

Callow. *Inexperienced, immature, untrained, naive*

Carnage. *Killing, slaughter, mass destruction, havoc massmurder*

Chandra. *The moon in the Hindi language*

Chided. *Scold, tell someone off*

Churlish. *Rude, mean, unfriendly*

Column. *An upright pillar, vertical, tall narrow shape cyclinder*

Comfrey. *A plant used for healing for thousands of years The latin meaning is 'to grow together'. It is thought to have protective magical qualities for a traveller*

Composure. *Feeling calm, in control of yourself not emotional*

Complacent. *Showing smug, uncritical satisfaction with your achievements*

Compound. *A thing that is made up of two or more separate things or to make something worse*

Concise. *Giving a lot of information clearly and in a few words*

Confer. *Give to, present with, honour with, discuss, talk*

Conspire. *Make secret plans with others, plot, plan to make something negative*

Contract. *Make smaller, decrease, shrink*

Contract. *Enter into a legal agreement, sign a legal document*

Convoluted. *Very twisted, complicated, complex, intricate, confusing, serpentine, tortuous*

Copse. *A small group of trees, thicket, grove, wood*

Crankily. *Bad tempered and disagreeable, erratic, to move or start, travel*

Crater. *A large bowl shaped cavity in the ground*

Crone. *In modern Wiccan or pagan groups crone is the triple goddess in the form of maiden/ mother/ crone and* is honoured and wise

Crone. *An old, withered, evil woman with magical powers*

Culprit. *Bad person, person responsible for a crime or misdeed, wrong doer*

Dappled. *Marked with round spots or patches*

Daunting. *Causing fear, discouragement, disheartening, Intimidating*

Defiance. *Open resistance, bold disobedience*

Deflator. *Make someone lose confidence, make smaller, lower*

Demise. *Death*

Derangement. *Feel disturbed, insane, mentally unwell, Cause to act in an irregular way*

Derided. *To ridicule, have contempt for, look down on*

Diligently. *Careful, using a lot of effort and attention in a job or task. Constant effort to accomplish something, persistent*

Distraught. *Deeply worried, upset, anxious, agitated crazed, distracted*

Domain. *Area of territory, owned by authority or ruler*

Dregs. *A small amount at the bottom of something*

Dwindle. *Reduce, lessen in size or amount, decrease, sink, Fewer,lower, deplete*

Enmeshed. *To become tangled or trapped in something To be involved in something difficult to get out of*

Fable. *A short story with animals as characters with A moral meaning*

Feat. *An achievement that requires courage and skill*

Fecund. *Capable of producing new growth or offspring, highly fertile, rich, lush, fruitful*

Feeble. *Lacking in Strength*
Fervent. *Displaying passionate, strong intensity*
Fester. *Become rotten, septic. A situation to worsen from neglect*
Fetid. *Stinking, smelly, rank, foul, unpleasant smell*
Fey. *Giving an impression of vague unworldliness, fated to die*
Fleet. *Quick, swift, rushed, brief, short, sudden*
Foliage. *Plant leaves*
Forlorn. *Sad, miserable, lonely, abandoned depressed, gloomy*

Guardian. *A person who protects and defends*
Grimace. *Scowling face, frown*

Hamper. *To prevent something from happening or Progressing*
Harbringer. *A person or thing that announces or signals The approach or start of something*
Hindrance. *Obstacle, block, delay, a thing that provides resistance or obstruction*
Hostile. *Intense dislike, aggressive, warlike, Showing or feeling opposition*
Hurtle. *Move at high speed in an uncontrolled way*

Impending. *About to happen, menacing threat*
Inclement. *Unpleasant weather*
Inebriated. *Drunk*
In lieu. *Instead of, to replace or substitute something*

Lichen. *They can be over 8000 years old and live on rock or bark. Plant like organisms that consist of algae and fungi. This is symbiosis where they live together as one*

Loam. *Fertile soil of clay and sand containing Humus (leaves and plants that have decomposed)*
Lament. *A passionate expression of grief or sorrow moaning, sobbing, crying*

Mace. *A spice made from the dried shell of nutmeg*
Magnanimous. *Generous, forgiving, handsome, kindly noble, big hearted*
Manically. *Crazy, mad, wacky, insane*
Meagre. *Lacking in quality or quantity, scant, limited, restricted, poor, puny, underweight*
Mesmerized. *Capture the complete attention of someone, transfixed, spellbound, hypnotize, dazzle*
Midden. *Rubbish heap, refuse, dunghill*
Mirth. *Amusement, laughter, cheerfulness, glee, happy, joyful*

Naga. *A member of a semi-divine race, part human part cobra, in Hindu mythology. Linked to mystical initiation. In some Hindu sects a naked wandering ascetic who carry arms and weapons as mercenaries*
Nark. *Angry, annoy, displeasure*
Nettle. *Plant used worldwide in ancient times and today Nettle fibres have been found in burial cloths from the Bronze age. It was thought to be a threshold between life and death. It is nutricious, high in iron and contains protein, vitamins and minerals. It can be drank as a tea to help clear infection, arthritus and allergies.*
Niche. *A comfortable, suitable position in life or employment.*

Ominous. *Worrying feeling or impression that something bad is going to happen. Threatening, sinister,* *menacing*

Orb. *Round, spherical object, globe,circle*

Peckish. *Feeling slightly hungry*
Pestle. *A heavy tool used with a mortar (container or bowl) Used to grind spices and herbs*
Petrified. *Very frightened, frozen with fear*

Queasy. *Feeling sick, nauseous, worried*
Quartz. *A hard mineral that can be colourless or white*

Rapturous. *Feeling pleasure, joy, enthusiasm, blissful Happy*
Raven. *An intelligent black bird with a history linked to Celts, the Welsh, Christians, Vikings and North American Indians.*
Raze. *To completely destroy, tear down and demolish*
Replete. *Filled or well supplied, well provided, stocked overflowing*
Rollicking. *Happening with a lot of fast action and noise*

Scold. *Tell someone off. To rebuke*
Shimmy. *To move effortlessly and glide with a swaying movement*
Sinewy. *Muscular, powerful, athletic, tough, firm*
Slumber. *Sleep, doze, drowse*
Smote. *Strike or hit hard. To deliver a blow or injure*
Sober. *Not affected by alcohol. Not drunk. Clear headed sensible, steady, dignified*
Sorrel. *A herbaceous perennial plant used since ancient times as a food and herbal medicine. Used in salads and soup. Fresh leaves could be applied to wounds, skin rashes or burns. It has high levels of vitamin C, It has been used*

to dye clothes and remove rust and mould stains

Spatter. *Cover with drops or spots of something. Splash, spray, sprinkle*

Spelt. *An old kind of wheat eaten as a health food*

Spur. *A thing that encourages someone, move, drive forward, propel, urge, to give incentive to*

Stark. *Severe or bare in appearance. Crisp, sharp obvious, distinct, defined*

Strife. *Angry or bitter disagreement, bad feeling friction, conflict, disharmony, dispute*

Sublime. *Beautiful, excellent, noble, glorious, complete magnificent*

Succumb. *Give in, give way, surrender, be overwhelmed by, fail to resist, submit*

Sully. *Spoil, damage the purity of, make impure disgrace, dishonour*

Sumptuous. *Luxurious, grand, splendid, rich, costly expensive, impressive*

Surya. *Sun in Hindi language*

Swan. *There are many myths and legends from around the world regarding swans. They symbolise beauty, love, grace and protection. In Hinduism they represent the connection between the material world and the spirit world.*

Tomb. *A large, underground chamber for burying the dead, grave, burial pit or mound*

Traverse. *Travel across or through, journey over pass over, move back, forth and sideways*

Turmoil. *Confusion, disturbance, uncertainty, trouble, Disruption, upheaval*

Udgitha. *Chanting, singing in Sanskrit (Aum), an ancient language*

Uncouth. *Lacking good manners, common, low, coarse crude, gross, hooligan, rough*

Vagrant. *Someone without a home who wanders from place to place. A tramp or drifter, nomad, roving, rootless, moving*

Verdant. *Green with grass and vegetation, leafy*

Warily. *Carefully, cautiously, to be on your guard, Watchfully*

Weevil. *A small beetle with a long snout*

Wreak. *Inflict, to cause damage or harm violently*

Writhe. *Making twisting turning movements, to wriggle, Squirm, jerk, to respond with great emotional discomfort*

Yew tree. *A native tree in Britain, sacred to Druids. In Celtic culture and Christianity it represented death and resurrection. Used in medieval times to make bows*

Bibliography of Images

1. A beautiful palace and a bridge over the river. Royalty-free stock vector images ID: 360879104. Artist: Danussa. Source: Shutterstock.
2. Vector engraving illustration of highly detailed hand drawn fly isolated on white background. Royalty-free stock vector images ID: 303090809. Artist: Andrey Oleynik. Source: Shutterstock.
3. Portrait of the surreal human witch girl with a head open and full of night moth butterflies. Dreamy sci-fi, tattoo art. Isolated vector illustration. Trendy T-shirt print. Halloween, weird sticker. Royalty-free stock vector images ID: 1069000847. Artist: Katja Gerasiomva. Source: Shutterstock.
4. King in the Breeze. Artist: Karen Stone.
5. Vector Double exposure, bear for your design, wildlife concept. Royalty-free stock vector images ID: 459889465. Artist: Mirifada. Source: Shutterstock.
6. Vintage 19th century drawing of a Kakapo common known as the owl parrot - Picture from Meyers Lexikon book (written in German language) published in 1908 Leipzig - Germany. Royalty-free stock photo ID: 103406933. Source: Shutterstock.
7. Bee. Artist: Karen Stone.
8. Sketch of bird for tattoo. Line art. Royalty-free stock vector images ID: 539764636. Artist: Amanda Geller. Source: Shutterstock.
9. Owl. Royalty-free stock illustration ID: 489500263. Artist: InkKing. Source: Shutterstock.
10. Spider. Artist: Jenny Jop.
11. Owl Carrying Girl. Artist: Jenny Jop.

12. Black and white engrave isolated monkey. Royalty-free stock vector images ID: 771329767. Artist: EvgenyTuraev. Source: Shutterstock.
13. Donkey. Artist: Karen Stone.
14. Kidnapper's Head. Artist: Karen Stone.
15. Falling From Broom. Artist: Jenny Jop.
16. Hare. Artst: Jenny Jop.
17. Design hand drawn sketch with a female with long hair and a flower wreath. Bride. Set of wedding vintage design elements, designers toolkit. Vector illustration. Royalty-free stock vector images ID: 275935925. Artist: HaHanna. Source: ShutterStock.
18. Sketch of small rat. Vector Illustration. Royalty-free stock vector images ID: 410423338. Artist: DianaFinch. Source: Shutterstock.
19. Snake & Toad. Artist: Karen Stone.
20. Witch Head - Karen Stone.
21. Hawk Outline. Artist: Jenny Jop.
22. Attacking eagle tattoo. Royalty-free stock vector images ID: 99815441. Artist: Vecktor. Source: ShutterStock.
23. Wizard with Lizard. Artist: Karen Stone.
24. Unicorn. Royalty-free stock vector images ID: 380900608. Artist: EtherMary. Source: Shutterstock.
25. Tortoise and Goblins. Artist: Karen Stone.
26. Tree with Face. Artist: Karen Stone.
27. The original drawing of birds on white paper, White-bellied Woodpecker. Royalty-free stock illustration ID: 247447810. Artist: forest71. Source: Shutterstock.
28. Riding Unicorn. Artist: Karen Stone.
29. Fairy tale characters, trolls, old tree, goblins, monsters, graphic illustration. Royalty-free stock illustration ID: 400575346. Artist: Barandash

Karandashich. Source: Shutterstock.

30. Stylized hand drawing crow. Decorative bird. Hand drawn raven or rook. Black and white drawing by hand. Witchcraft, voodoo magic attribute. Royalty-free stock illustration ID: 493873339. Artist: Golden Shrimp. Source: Shutterstock.

31. Orangutan (PithecusSatyrus) - Vintage illustration from Meyers Konversations-Lexikon 1897. Royalty-free stock photo ID: 91640768. Source: Shutterstock.

32. High detailed illustration of an old oak tree with a root system, hand drawn, vector. Royalty-free stock vector images ID: 787230481. Artist: Grop. Source: Shutterstock.

33. Hand of witch with fire. Mystic character. Royalty-free stock vector images ID: 1157467405. Artist: Gorbash Varvara. Source: Shutterstock.

34. Snake Man. Artist: Karen Stone.

35. Witch's cauldron and butterflies, magical thing, Wiccan magic. Royalty-free stock vector images ID: 1198717948. Artist: Eldi D. Source: Shutterstock.

36. Handsome male elf character with long hair holding and magic sword. Royalty-free stock vector images ID: 735619708. Artist: Natasha_Mor. Source: Shutterstock.

37. Black and white engrave isolated pig vector illustration. Royalty-free stock vector images ID: 1070981273. Artist: EvgenyTuraev. Source: Shutterstock.

38. Wolf silhouette on forest background. Royalty-free stock vector images ID: 518656711. Artist: ElemenTxD. Source: Shutterstock.

39. Totem eagle, wolf, fox and owl illustration for creating sketches of tattoos, printing on clothes, design of

posters and leaflets. Royalty-free stock vector images ID: 725969953. Artist: Filkusto. Source: Shutterstock.

40. Wizard With Dragon. Artist: Karen Stone.

41. Vector illustration of side view roaring brown bear silhouette. Royalty-free stock vector images ID: 794739172. Artist: Norma Meoni. Source: Shutterstock.

42. Witch's hand. Royalty-free stock illustration ID: 1192490224. Artist: Olga Toshka. Source: Shutterstock.

43. Deer with antler like tree. Royalty-free stock vector images ID: 82009303. Artist: Muamu. Source: Shutterstock.

44. Hand drawn illustration of shaman woman in cloak with raven in hand and deer skull on the head. Royalty-free stock vector images ID: 612116171. Artist: A. Wilton. Source: Shutterstock.

45. Hand drawn linear black and white sketch of a medieval Indian prince, rajah or sultan. Royalty-free stock vector images ID: 1042209580. Artist: Eroshka. Source: Shutterstock.

46. Beautiful romantic skull with crown and elegant wreath of flowers. Ink on aged card vintage background. Royalty-free stock vector images ID: 721863391. Artist: Marta Leo. Source: Shutterstock.

47. Fairy tale characters, trolls, old tree, goblins, monsters, graphic illustration. Royalty-free stock illustration ID: 402508981. Artist: BarandashKarandashich. Source: Shutterstock.

Voices in audio recording
Narrator and author Karen Stone
Thank you to Micky Waters (Donkey turned Unicorn)
Harrison Perks (The warrior)
Anthony John (The king and kidnapper)
Paul Needham (The swan and lark)
Simon Mckay (The tortoise, snake and elf)
Julie Mckay (Brown rat, shaman mother eagle and tree)
Dave Mckay (The wolf)

Bibliography
Website Trees for life
'Faeries' by Brian Froud

Lightning Source UK Ltd.
Milton Keynes UK
UKHW041548280419
341738UK00002B/4/P